12 Cartoonists on Their Worlds of Humor

Hold That Thought

12 Cartoonists on Their Worlds of Humor

Hold That Thought

Edited by David Endelman

LESS
WORDS
PRESS

This cartoon collection is a compilation of works contributed by multiple cartoonists. Each individual author retains the copyright to their respective work. The names of the authors and the titles of their contributions are listed below:

Chapter 1: Isabella Bannerman* © 2023 Isabella Bannerman
Chapter 2: David Gomberg © 2023 David Gomberg
Chapter 3: Suzy Becker © 2023 Suzy Becker
Chapter 4: David Endelman © 2023 David Endelman
Chapter 5: Jim Shoenbill © 2023 Jim Shoenbill
Chapter 6: Jun Frogosa © 2023 Jun Frogosa
Chapter 7: Catherine Holmes © 2023 Catherine Holmes
Chapter 8: Theresa Henry © 2023 Theresa Henry
Chapter 9: Sam Lay © 2023 Sam Lay
Chapter 10: Beverley Kort © 2023 Beverley Kort
Chapter 11: Rose Anne Prevec © 2023 Rose Anne Prevec
Chapter 12: Ed Himelblau © 2023 Ed Himelblau

*Following cartoons from Six Chix used with permission:
Six Chix © 2020 Isabella Bannerman, Distributed by King Features Syndicate, Inc. ("Rabbits" cartoon)
Six Chix © 2021 Isabella Bannerman, Distributed by King Features Syndicate, Inc. ("Dolores" cartoon)
Six Chix © 2022 Isabella Bannerman, Distributed by King Features Syndicate, Inc. ("Knock Yourself Out" and "Bookstore")
Six Chix © 2023 Isabella Bannerman, Distributed by King Features Syndicate, Inc. ("Relish" and "Cat Scientists")

Following cartoons originally appeared in Narrative Magazine and used with permission:
"Universe" cartoon by David Gomberg
"Octopus" cartoon by Catherine Holmes

Cover Design by David Gomberg
Front Cover Cartoon by Catherine Holmes

Published by Less Words Press, an imprint of Wavomedia
2060 D Avenida de Los Arboles #590
Thousand Oaks, CA 91362
LessWordsPress.com

First Edition, 2023

ISBN: 978-1-947028-04-3

Printed in the United States of America

Special thanks to David Gomberg whose sketch inspired this book.

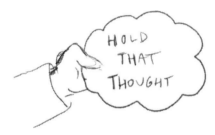

Table of Contents

Introduction

By David Endelman, Editor

I have a secret to share. In kindergarten, my prospects were not bright. I couldn't sit still unless I was daydreaming and/or doodling. My teacher faced a dilemma: either pass me with little justification or have me in her class for another year. The inevitable parent-teacher conference occurred, and a compromise was reached. I could pass into first grade, if my parents and I agreed not to tell anyone the name of my kindergarten teacher. Somehow, that experience helped catapult me into becoming a cartoonist and now the editor of this book.

Of course, I am not at all alone with wrestling with the rambunctiousness of creativity. We all need to share a laugh or a smile at whatever, to share a mischievous idea, and to pause for thought. Why? Because we all have regular encounters with irony and absurdity that challenge us to smile and to make something fun of it. Probably, that is why cartoons began.

Now, I want you to meet some of my favorite cartoonists. Most of us hang out on Instagram where we can post whatever in the world we feel like. Best of all, real people can see our work and comment anyway they like. Somehow, this social-media interplay provides an important balance for seriously offbeat cartoonists.

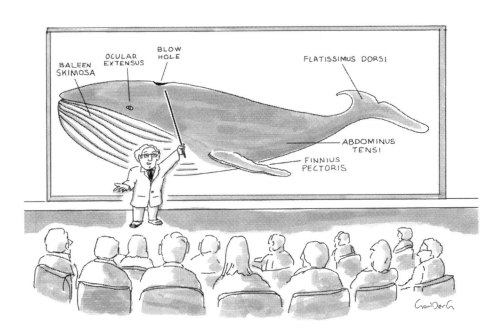

"...and here's where we ran out of Latin."

"Honey, it's a monster-sized snail.
We should pack at a comfortable pace, then flee."

Suzy Becker
Central Massachusetts, USA

Maker of Fun & Widgets of Wonderment

Suzy Becker is an author/illustrator and *New Yorker* cartoonist (not cartoonSist, so far they've taken one). She began her illustratious career as an award-winning copywriter, then founded The Widget Factory, a greeting card company. Her first book was the internationally bestselling *All I Need to Know I Learned from My Cat*, now available in the Double-Platinum edition *All I Need to Know I Learned from My Cat (And Then Some)*. She has since written and illustrated nine other books for kids and grownups, including the graphic medicine memoirs, *I Had Brain Surgery, What's Your Excuse?* and *One Good Egg*. She has also ghostwritten a couple of books—one won a James Beard award.

Suzy's had other jobs that make cartooning seem normal, like operating a line of machines at a synthetic mohair factory, folding submarine plans, or teaching eighth graders. She lives with her family and their two well-meaning dogs in the midst of central Massachusetts.

See more about Suzy at suzybecker.com and @suzybecker on Instagram.

"It's not you. It's me."

"*I liked it better when we each had our own place.*"

"I'm a high-functioning recluse."

"Our verdict, your honor..."

"What ball through yonder window breaks...?"

"Let's see, yeah, so, I could definitely have that for you by..."

"She's going to be an influencer when she grows up."

David Endelman
Los Angeles Area, CA, USA

Cartoons of Signs and Cymbals

Dave has done it all: dishwashing, stock clerking, burger flipping, map folding, map making, and nap taking. These activities through different times and places provided character-building experiences for an emerging cartoonist.

The Greater Los Angeles area, famous for wildfires, earthquakes, and floods is where Dave calls home because he likes sunny weather and Hawaiian shirts. A career in cartography along with keen freeway driving, suburban living, and epic surfing attempts have somehow led Dave to a serious contemplation of signs and the creation of his *Sign Garden* cartoon series. Evident perils of being overly attentive to signs can be seen in his work and his unbelievably pretentious use of the word "semiotics."

Dave lives with his wife, author Gail Small, and an imaginary, but surprisingly messy, Saint Bernard dog. Dave's cartoons can be seen on the coolest of refrigerators. His book, *Different Signs: Cartoons from Sign Garden* can be found on Amazon.

On Instagram find his work @davidendelman
and for more info go to davidendelman.com

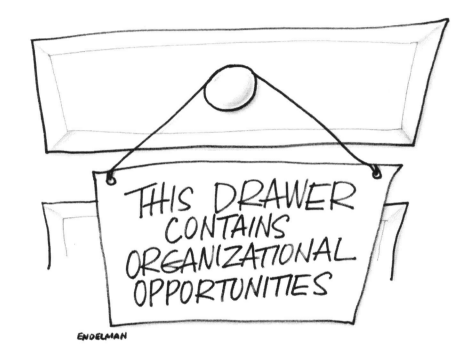

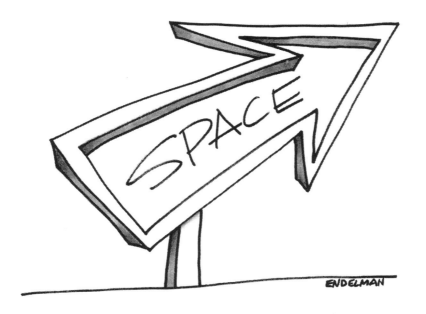

Jim Shoenbill
Durham County, NC, USA

Purveyor of Small-Batch, Artisanal Cartoons & Humor

Jim Shoenbill channels odd thoughts into cartoons, writing, T-shirt designs, and the occasional interpretive movement. His mission is to brighten your day with positive humor. Jim's cartoons have appeared in numerous publications and Oatmeal Studios greeting cards.

Jimmy, as he was then known, grew up in Wisconsin, drawing constantly and learning about humor by observing his large family and watching far too many sitcoms. Jim entered college as an art major but unexpectedly emerged with a couple of degrees in computer science, leading to a long and productive career in business and technology.

Back in 2012, Jim tried cartooning as a way to connect his background in drawing to the strange jokes and narratives piling up in his brain. Finding it to be a boon to mental health, and cheaper than both golf and therapy, he has since embraced humor and creativity as central components of a happy existence.

Jim is also a dad; he has cargo shorts and a fanny pack and is not afraid to use them. He resides in North Carolina and is a member of the Southeast Chapter of the National Cartoonists Society. Jim's collection of comics from 2012-2019, *The Big Book of Magic Coffee Hair Cartoons*, is available from Amazon.

For more go to jimshoenbill.com or @jimshoenbill on Instagram.

"No one else in my family got out of the garden,
much less made it to college."

"In the event of a water landing, your seat cushions may be used as flotation devices. And, your tray tables may be used to bash sharks."

"Don't think I can get you a job here
just because we used to sleep together."

"You were texting, weren't you?!?"

"...that drug from the commercial with
the old guys surfing and the marching band
and the sad woman who buys a puppy...
is that right for me?"

Bucky's dream of becoming a stand-up comedian
ended abruptly the very first time
he stepped into the spotlight.

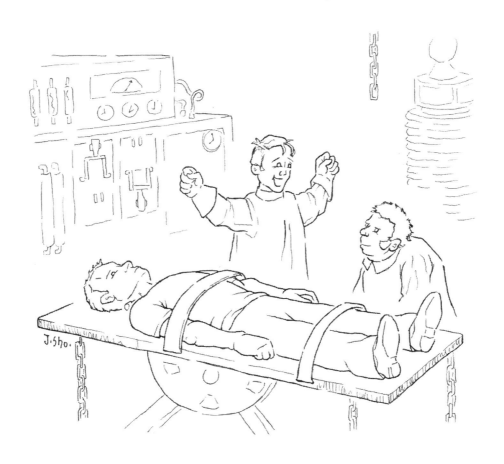

"It's alive!! My terrifying undead monstrosity is alive!!
Now, let's get him into a sport coat."

"Remember, everyone—it's not too late
to sign up for our AdventureMiles credit card!"

"That's about me, isn't it?"

Jun Frogosa
Düsseldorf, Germany

Beyond First Impressions

The first impression never gets any chance with Jun. His search for the second view of whatever topic strikes his attention is driven by a deep sense of curiosity. Fortunately, he was able to keep the fire of curiosity burning beyond his childhood and the rigor of a formal education.

Jun seeks to create cartoons which are intriguing, while having a splash of humor at the same time. Curiosity is the essential spark which leads to his imaginative juxtapositions and re-inventions of the seemingly boring and familiar icons of our modern culture.

Having training in graphic arts has been tremendously instrumental in helping Jun develop his simple, yet enigmatic style to create thought-provoking cartoons.

Explore more @jun.frogosa on Instagram.

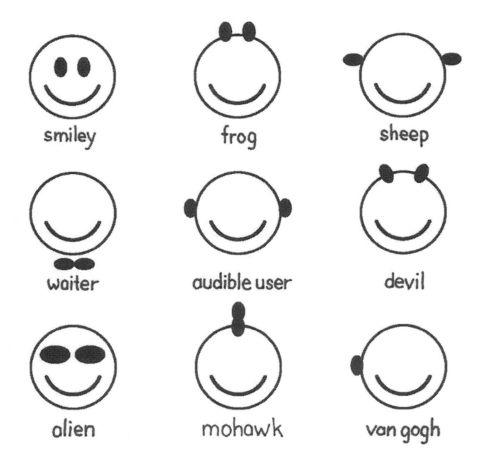

smiley   frog   sheep

waiter   audible user   devil

alien   mohawk   van gogh

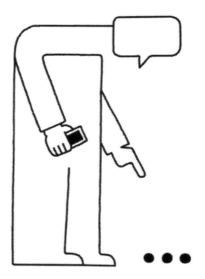

DON'T WORRY. BE HAPPY

I CAN'T LET GO OF SUMMER

Catherine Holmes
Vancouver Island, BC, Canada

An Explorer of Art on an Island of Humor

Catherine Holmes is a cartoonist/painter living on Vancouver Island, Canada. She grew up in Ottawa, Ontario. Catherine spent a few years at the Ontario College of Art (now OCADU) in Toronto. While living in Northern Ontario she received her bachelor's degrees in arts and education from Lakehead University in the late 1980's. She then began traveling overseas with her husband, an exploration geologist, and their two children.

She has worked as a part time art teacher, a visiting artist in the schools, and freelance illustrator. Her work as an illustrator laid the groundwork for cartooning, as much of this earlier work had the whimsy of her cartoons today minus the captions. Inspiration for her cartoons comes from everyday family/life/situations, her travels, rescue cat, and also from the world of the absurd. A practice of daily drawing keeps the ideas flowing, some funny ones even make it off the drawing board.

Catherine set out a few years back to find more humor in her work. She's still looking, but it's a worthwhile journey; she highly recommends it.

To view more of her work, visit catherinemholmes.com
or go to @catherine__holmes on Instagram.

"This noun ain't big enough for the two of us."

"Trade ya."

"Seriously?"

"Do you Ingrid, take this clay, to have and to mold into the partner of your wildest dreams?"

"No seriously, what's happening?"

"*Buzz, buzz, buzz-buzz, b#$z, buzz, BUZZ, buzz.*"

"Do you mind if I exfoliate?"

CMH

DEEP-STEEP DIVING

Theresa Henry
Vancouver, BC, Canada

Flashy & Fashionable Fusion Humor

Theresa, a former art teacher, has been in the cartooning game off and on for several decades. In the 80's and 90's she had work featured in various cool indie publications such as: *Spatter*, *New Comics*, *Pox*, *Escape Magazine*, *Big Noise*, *True North*, *Giant Sized Mini Comics*, and *Adbusters*. She also contributed to magazines, weeklies, and books like Roz Warren's *What is This Thing Called Sex?*

Now fast forward to the new millennium; there was this pandemic thing so Theresa decided to take the unexpected free time to learn how to create cartoons digitally (it had been ink & paper back in the old-timey days). After badgering her kids about what Instagram was and how it worked, she finally launched her cartoon account @hotflashesandhangovers in May 2020. There, she has connected with an active, growing audience and an awesome community of fellow cartoonists. That's how she met the nice creators of this funny book!

Theresa lives in Vancouver, British Columbia with her family who may or may not resemble some of her cartoon characters in *Hotflashes & Hangovers*.

Find Theresa @hotflashesandhangovers on Instagram
and @cartoonishlady on TikTok.

COMMON ROMANTIC PROBLEMS
IN THE PUNK ROCK ERA.

TSK, TSK, JUDITH! WHEN YOU SAY, THERE'S 'A PLAGUE OF
AIRBORNE OCTOPUSES OUTSIDE', DON'T YOU ACTUALLY MEAN TO
SAY THAT THERE IS 'A PLAGUE OF AIRBORNE *OCTOPI* OUTSIDE'?

THAT FATAL MOMENT WHEN GLORIA REALIZED IT HAD
BEEN UNWISE TO WAIT FOR THE OTHER SHOE TO DROP.

POOR EARL WOULD SOON LEARN THE HARD
WAY ABOUT THE LAW OF SUPPLY AND DEMAND

119

GLITCH IN THE MATRIX? YES, I'VE HEARD OF THE TERM. WHY DO YOU ASK?

Sam Lay
Singapore

On an Oasis of Quiet Humor

Sam Lay is a Singapore-based cartoonist. His practice explores and satirizes our universal experience where the humor of everyday life is celebrated on a level that everyone can enjoy and understand. Sam lets his cartoon works deliver the narrative or punchline without the accompanying text or speech of conventional cartoon art. Drawing since 1995, he maintains his practice through a monthly cartoon column on *Lianhe Zaobao*, a leading Mandarin newspaper published in Singapore.

In 2020, supported by the National Arts Council, Sam created over 200 cartoons as part of *The Oddly Sequential* project, an initiative to promote the awareness of pantomime cartoons to the audiences in Singapore. In 2021, Sam started the project *Life in a Notebook*, where he strikes the creative chemistry between his illustrations and everyday life by incorporating common household objects into his cartoons. The project was subsequently turned into an exhibition the following year. Passionate about the cartooning craft, Sam continues to create a visual world that is a little bit familiar, a little bit new, and where everyone is welcome.

For more, visit oddlysequential.com or @oddlysequential.sl on Instagram.

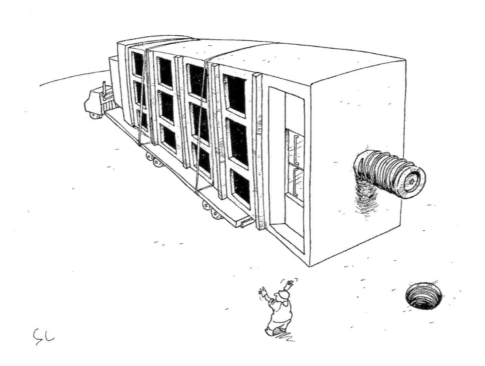

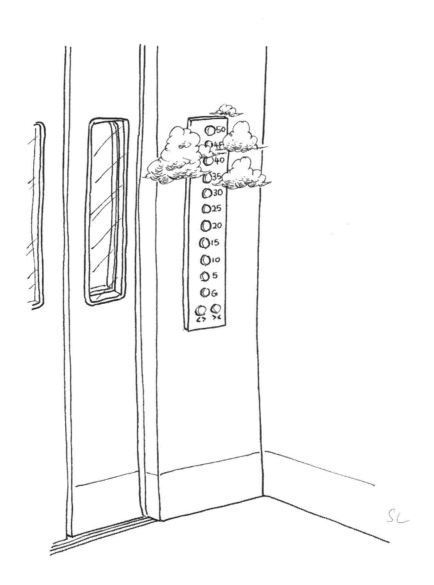

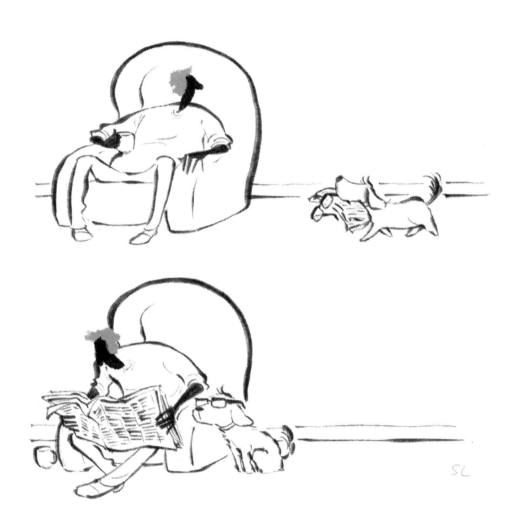

Beverley Kort
Vancouver, BC, Canada

Life with a Cartoonist's Touch & a Psychologist's Mind

Beverley Kort is a cartoonist who happens to also be a registered psychologist with a private practice in Vancouver, BC. She combines her love of helping people with her love of art. Beverley enjoys turning everyday struggles about modern life and the idiosyncrasies of her profession with, she hopes, witty and relatable cartoons.

Humor has always been a part of her approach to life and to therapy. She is excited about how cartooning combines her two passions.

Beverley's work has appeared in the *Hungry Zine*, *Asparagus*, *Spring Rider*, and she is a recurring contributor to the *Jewish Independent Newspaper* in Vancouver.

Beverley has 3 children and 4 grandchildren. Her 5 year-old grandson has already started telling her what he thinks is funny and to make a cartoon of it.

Her work can be found @bkort4 on Instagram.

Fred tried to get his ducks in a row.

BKot

"We've been hacked!"

DINNER AND A SHOW

"It's exhausting being all things to one human."

"I think I'm too giving."

She slept well under her favorite covers.

*"There is only room for one cartoonist
on this island."*

Rose Anne Prevec
Dundas, ON, Canada

Cartoonist of Creatures of Comedy

Rose Anne's cartoons were inspired by the Canadian wildlife she encountered during daily tromps through the conservation area near her Southern Ontario home. Her muses—raccoons, deer, opossums, and more—followed her home, ate everything en route, trotted out their quirky talents, challenged idioms, and demanded inky portraits. The call of nature was insistent...pushy, even.

Over time, Rose Anne's repertoire has expanded to include a wider cast of more peculiar characters—humans. Any resemblance to real persons is purely coincidental and definitely not drawn from her career in communications and art galleries.

She illustrated the *Toby the Pet Therapy Dog* book series, and her cartoons appear sporadically in print and regularly @groundhog_hill on Instagram.

Rose Anne and her family, including a fierce ginger cat, live on the edge of the wild.

For more about Rose Anne go to www.groundhoghill.ca

"I'm going to call them 'slippers.'"

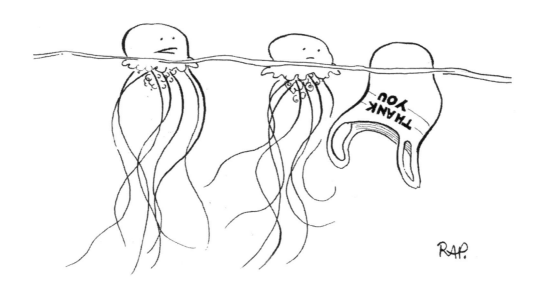

"Not much of a talker, is he?"

*"Tell Mary a secret and you may as well
be telling five people."*

"Do you see the one who jumped you?"

"*I used to envy it, but then I realized its insides
are a roiling mass of anxiety.*"

"At this intersection it's only a matter of time."

"Finally! A distraction from my inner demons."

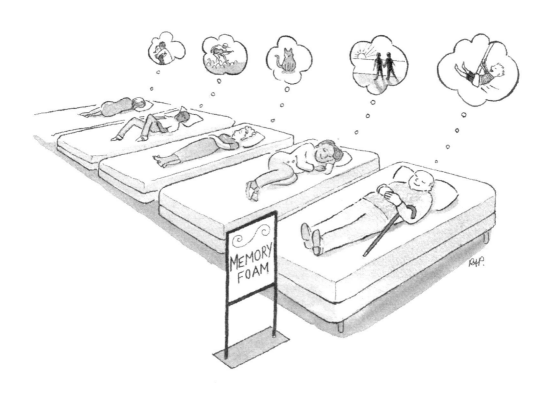

"Do you play?"

Ed Himelblau
San Luis Obispo, CA, USA

Scientist on the Biology of Funny Stuff

Ed Himelblau is a cartoonist living in San Luis Obispo, California. Ed is a professor in the Biological Sciences Department at California Polytechnic State University. He teaches courses in genetics and botany. His research focuses on the DNA of the plant species, *Brassica oleracea*. In other words, he studies mutant broccoli.

Ed's earliest art influence was Charles Schultz and he avidly collected *Peanuts* books from yard sales and used bookstores. Ed's family subscribed to *The New Yorker* and he came to love the single-panel cartoon format, especially the cartoons of Roz Chast and George Booth.

Ed started drawing cartoons as a graduate student in Madison, Wisconsin in the 1990s. His cartoons focused on life in the science laboratory, a theme he still explores in his cartoons today. In 2019 he began submitting cartoons to *The New Yorker*. His first cartoon was published in the magazine in 2021.

See more at himelblau.com or @himelblog on Instagram.

HIMELBLAU

"It's OK! He's friendly!"

"When I don't have any ideas for dinner
I just end up staring into the freezer"

"Science has much to learn about the poison ivy genome."

"He's focused more on self discovery."

MANICONDA!

"Two birds, one stone... Do the math!"

"Well...at least he was wearing his safety glasses."

*"Sometimes I walk him. Sometimes Larry walks him.
But no one's keeping score."*

"Spoiler alert."

"The deep ocean holds many mysteries...as does love."

"How does she make it look so effortless?"

"*Just in case I need to jot down an idea in the night.*"

Extra Special Thought

Thank you for taking the time to hold on

to this collection of thoughts of humor.

The 12 cartoonists in this book thank you

for sharing smiles with us.

Made in United States
Troutdale, OR
12/08/2023

15526949R00102